Dedicated to all the kings who spend a little extra time on the throne.

While Daddy Was Pooping

Written by Dani Rowland

Illustrated by Chris Rowland

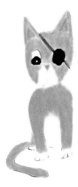

It happened after breakfast one sunny Saturday. Mommy started cleaning, and I began to play. I shouted, "Daddy play with me! We'll be an army troop!" He winced a bit, and as he split, he said, "I have to poop!"

Mommy chuckled softly as she started drying dishes. She said, " You can do tons of things while Daddy feeds the fishes."

And so I stood there planning all the things that I could do, with all that time I have to kill while Daddy takes a poo.

While Daddy was pooping...
I built a rocket ship. I flew it high into the
sky. It was a pleasant trip.

I journeyed far beyond the stars and went right past the Sun, but then I thought, "Good grief, it's hot," and decided I was done.

While Daddy was pooping...
I sailed across the sea. With an eye patch
and treasure map, a pirate now I be.

"X marks the spot!" My parrot croaked as we bounced upon the blue. We found the jewels, then sailed back home to go try something new.

"HE'S TAKING FOREVER!"

I thought to myself, so I tapped on the door...

Dad said, "Not now, stand back, I say! I think
I have some more!"

While Daddy was pooping...
I did a scuba dive. How marvelous were the
colors and the creatures there that thrive.

I bobbed and floated carelessly until I saw a shark. I swam away, quite fast, I'd say, those teeth would leave a mark.

While Daddy was pooping to the jungle, I did go. To play with monkeys in the trees while swinging to and fro.

I saw a bush begin to move, with eyes that seemed to glow. "A panther, YIKES!" Before he strikes, I think I'd better go.

Then finally we heard a flush, the faucet made a hiss, and out the door came Daddy saying, "HEY, What did I miss?"

Made in the USA
Middletown, DE
12 September 2023

38397113R00015